S0-BEV-183

Living With Illness

By
HUGH CALKINS

THOMAS
MORE
PRESS

Copyright © 1973 by the Thomas More Association. All rights reserved.
Printed in the United States of America. No part of this publication
may be reproduced, stored in a retrieval system, or transmitted, in any
form or by any means, electronic, mechanical, photocopying, recording,
or otherwise without the prior written permission of the publisher,
the Thomas More Association, 180 N. Wabash Avenue,
Chicago, Illinois 60601

Contents

For Openers

This will not be a sad book, although it deals with sad events. Neither will it be preachy, although it is so easy for a former missionary and present hospital chaplain to wax eloquent about illness. Of magic or occult remedies, I have none. And who can write or read chins-up stuff these days? We are all glad just to cope with or even survive illness.

This is a book for those who suffer from illness and for those who minister to their needs—especially for the patients and their ministers who live hourly and daily with protracted illnesses. These may be long-term handicaps or recoveries, deep-seated emotional or mental problems, critical-sick behavior problems, chronic or even terminal illness, the helplessly blind or crippled, the retarded and damaged-at-birth illness, or other types equally as serious. We are not dealing here with "just bad" flu, sore back, or the miseries.

In a society as sick as ours, each of us is either the suffering patient or the ministering nurse—unless we have copped out and are not really alive to others. This would make us sickest of all—patients unaware that we are ill. Through my printed words many an expert will speak to you. For the ministering I work at daily is to persons from five to ninety-five and they suffer from illnesses called mental, emotional, nervous, physical, organic—or some combination of these. They have taught me much that may be helpful to you, as we share the following pages.

What about you? How do you live with illness? How do you minister to the sick who need you? Let us try to renew our priorities in a mad world. Let us ponder together values that give suffering and dying genuine meaning. Maybe thoughts we share will intensify or even restore your deep commitment to others. This will not be because I have been there before you or because I know better responses than yours, but because these pages come from a concerned heart.

Ideally, this book should be the work of one of God's VIPs (very important people—my name for those carrying a big cross of pain). Why should I, in ruddy health now and most of my life, tackle these chapters that follow? So often patients have told many of us who minister to them: "You just don't know how awful this pain is." And we nod in agreement. Yet I know too that many a patient has begged us: "Tell them more about how it really is. Maybe they'll visit and be kinder. Let them know."

Then I recall an admonition from a then superbly healthy Albert Schweitzer laboring in jungle areas for neglected sick people: "Whoever is spared personal pain must feel himself called to help in diminishing the pain of others. We must all carry our share of the misery which lies upon the world" (*The World of Albert Schweitzer* by Erica Anderson, Harper & Row).

So from true stories, from insights passed on by sick people, from rock-solid, heartfelt truths, from secrets of suffering heard from parched lips, I proffer to you an account in living with and ministering to illness. And I hope these pages will help both the sick and the well to grow in *compassion*. This beautiful word means true sadness caused by the thought of someone else's pain. It means to suffer with, or in union with, someone in pain—to suffer with Christ as Mary did at the Crucifixion. It brings one to learn from Christ and Mary how all who suffer and minister to pain are in some way working with Christ the Redeemer, as Mary did pre-eminently at the on-going task of redeeming the universe and each human being.

CHAPTER ONE

The Why of All Suffering

> Simeon blessed them and said to Mary his mother: "You
> see this child . . . destined to be a sign that is rejected . . .
> and a sword will pierce your own soul too . . . so that the
> secret thoughts of many will be laid bare."
>
> Luke 2: 34-35

Joseph and Mary followed the Jewish law
and they brought Jesus to Jerusalem to present him
to the Lord. Then, Simeon, who was a devout man
awaiting the consolation of Israel, proclaimed a prophetic blessing for Mary and her child: The prophetic
word will be a sign contradicted or accepted by many
—depending upon the faith-response of each man.
Mary, too, receives a foretaste of the role she will
play in the redemptive work of her Son. Her role will
involve the same kind of renunciation of self and
sacrificial obedience that are Christ's destiny.

But what a time to hear this bell tolling the burden of suffering Mary must bear. Just when she was doing everything right, according to the laws of her religion. Why would many of those in Israel reject Christ and bring about his death? Why would Mary, so loyal to all that God asked of her, endure such a deep sorrow? The answer lies clearly before us. Suffering lets us share in the redeeming work of Jesus.

As it did to Mary, so must suffering come to us— especially through illness and all that accompanies it. We often are surprised, hurt, even angry. "Why me? And why now, just when I'm living such a good life?" Or, "Why this innocent baby?" "Why this saintly, elderly person?" Such queries ring familiar in our ears. It is only human and natural to question, wonder or even try to flee the suffering of illness.

Perhaps you are a person who does not accept this argument for the *why* of suffering. Of course, any reasonable person of faith will allow for the various reasons offered by different religious groups, as humans grapple with the puzzling realities of illness. Yet, for those who read and ponder the revelation of

God throughout the Bible, as fulfilled in the New Testament, sharing with Christ and his chosen ones, like Mary, the ongoing redemption of the universe and of each human being remains the deepest and most meaningful response. But this belief results from faith, faith in God's plans for his world.

Human beings constantly search for meaning in life. And many a victim of war prisons or concentration camps can testify about illness, torture, dying daily and yet surviving: as Victor Frankl says, a human being who clearly knows his *why* to live can bear with almost any *how* to live.

Inevitably a moment comes when each human being is taught a basic truth about human existence. That basic truth is that to live involves suffering, but *to survive* means a person must find *meaning* in that suffering. If life has any purpose for each one of us —and how well this hits home when we endure illness—there must be a purpose in suffering and dying. True, each person must find that for himself: no man can really tell another convincingly what that purpose is. Once a persuasive purpose is found and the person accepts the responsibility the answer brings, that human being will grow in inner strength despite all indignities.

The persuasive purpose to endure the pain and loneliness of illness may arise from varied value judgments. These values may be present in deeply religious persons or persons with no religion. They may be at purely human and natural levels (for my children, for the wife I hope to see again, to save my buddy) or at supernatural levels (for the love of God, in fidelity to my marriage or priestly commitments, to save souls). Mostly they are a mixture of both. Let God sort them out.

We suggest all through this book that each patient and minister work steadily at seeing God's designs working through illness. Each person wrestling with suffering reaches his own level of understanding and acceptance. So many factors of mind, heart, soul, background, good or poor training, cultural values, personality levels of development, graces and blessings given by God, faith-responses made by the person—all or many of these at work in a given life-story result in myriad patterns. But we must all remember that through illness and all types of suffering we are able to participate with Jesus' redeeming work and share in his glory in heaven.

Each time we utter a cry of anguish in illness—a cry of *Why* and *When* and *How*—God is close to us, aware of all that troubles us. We must build our trust in God's knowing what he is doing by accepting our illness. Our vision will necessarily be limited for our response of acceptance is based upon faith—an assent to things not seen. And our strength comes from hope, trust that in his own way and time God will take care of each beloved son and daughter. We must especially endure because we know God loves each of us, and illness is one way that can lead us to love him. As a terminal cancer patient so succinctly said: "Those deep X-ray treatments are awful. But Calvary was awful for Jesus, wasn't it? It's my turn now to do something for Jesus."

Maybe in your own illness you have not yet come to see as clearly as that how close you are to God in living out the sacrifice of Jesus. But pray that you will.

Strive to think along those lines. Let reading from Scripture, your reflections on pain, your contacts with sick people of deep insight help you to grow in such awareness.

As Pope Paul VI said to sick and suffering people everywhere at the close of the Second Vatican Council: "We offer you the truth that alone responds to the mystery of suffering and affords . . . a solace that is without illusion. That truth demands faith in our identity with the Man of Sorrows . . . crucified for our sins and our salvation. . . . You are the aristocracy of the Kingdom of God. . . . And if you but choose to do so, you work out with him the world's salvation. This is the Christian understanding of suffering: it is the only one that puts your heart at rest."

One day at our own hospital not long ago, a badly crippled patient sat in his wheelchair next to me, as I played piano for the patients. "I'm a Catholic, Father," he said aloud. "But why did God let me be so ugly as this and suffer so much, just to punish me?" I answered: "Can you see why he asked his Son to be killed on a cross, though he loved him so much? And why he wants you to be like Jesus and suffer too?" Just then a college-age aide walked up and asked: "I heard his question. He always asks us that. What did you tell him?" When I said it all again, the aide queried: "Did you tell him *that*?" And he walked away, shaking his head as if I had spoken gibberish. And I thought again of Paul telling us how Calvary is a stumbling block and a folly.

Maybe my patient friend did not absorb the theology of coredemption just at that moment. Who knows? God, through grace-laden pain, may teach him far more about it than I will ever comprehend. No one suffers alone and no one suffers uselessly. Suffering people, no matter how tiny their awareness of eternal values, mirror most faithfully the image of Christ, since he chose to identify with even the least of brethren. That comes across crystal-clear in Matthew (ch. 25) where he deals with the standards to be applied at Judgment. And who says it better than Paul in his letter to the Colossians: "It makes me happy to suffer for you, as I am suffering now, and in my own body to do what I can to make up all that has still to be undergone by Christ for the sake of his body, the church" (Col 1: 24-25).

Think how valuable the infirm patients at our hospital are to all of us who are well. Some have been bedridden for as long as twenty years. Do they know, do they think of the meaning of illness explained above? Only God knows for sure, or in what manner. But somehow, in their very own way, they have found a meaning that makes sense and gives them courage to live another day. When we who are well visit or minister to patients, we must see Jesus suffering in their lives. And we must give kindness and compassionate understanding to them so that they come to see Christ's mercy in us.

You are never quite sure what response you will get from patients, so deeply realistic are they about illness. This is true in hospital wards, in home-care setups, rectories, any nursing facility. One patient

told a priest recently: "Well, that's great about what
Paul says. But I'm not exactly a religious man. I just
sure hope all this pain and misery does somebody
some good. All I want is to get better and get outta
here fast."

This is not exactly a faith-response, and maybe
within him there was precious little awareness of the
coredeeming-with-Christ motivation. Yet note the
emphasis upon hope, the meaning that made endur-
ance more bearable. It meant trust that God would
somehow use it all and that he would get better. We
all need hope to meet any trial. No wonder Dante in
his *Divine Comedy* put over the gate of hell: "Aban-
don hope, all you who enter."

The way in which any human being accepts what
might be called his fate (or what we call taking up his
cross) and his motivation rooted in faith, hope and
love show him to be brave, dignified and unselfish.
Suffering can add deeper meaning to a person's life
here on earth, most certainly in heaven. We should

all pray for ourselves and for those we seek to serve that we shall be *worthy* of our sufferings. It would be sad if we did not use them to full advantage.

Is this too lofty an approach, too unworldly and too far removed from the brutality of today's sick world? No, emphatically not. Unless we somehow put such values to work, dredge up from within us such motives, seek beyond ourselves such goals we will buckle under and choose fantasy worlds. And there lies madness, retreat from life, despair, slow suicides in drugs or booze, accident-chosen deaths. It is true that each person finds his own level of growth through illness but each person must find *meaning* in illness to rise above its agonies.

Perhaps at this very moment you should happen to set this book down to bring nursing services to your patient—a retarded child, an aging parent, a crippled marriage partner. Think about how all of this fits those who minister to illness. Be sure that all we have said of sacrificial love is true of those who give themselves in serving others, just as Mary showed her compassion toward Jesus with all her heart and mind while he suffered agonizing mental and physical pain. John the Apostle, an eyewitness tells us (using a strong word), *stood*—no heroics, no outcry, no swooning. Mary was there sharing, just as so many of you loyal nurses at home share, pray and sacrifice with ailing relatives and friends.

How many times we have all seen at parish Masses such ministering apostles helping their patients to the altar rail. Do we give heed to physical and spiritual service rendered as no hospital could ever do? No union wage scale could ever properly pay them. Working conditions are impossible by any "practical" standard. The "folly of the cross" described by Paul goes into their endless household chores and medical nursing. They are priest, doctor, lector, news commentator, cook, head dishwasher, laundress, nurse, lab technician—and tender-loving-care companion.

Oh, yes! Generally they have their head on straight about why they do all these works of mercy. They are motivated by compassion, love for neighbor and God, well aware of: "If you give even a cup of cold water in my name, you shall have an eternal reward." Like all of us, they grow weary of the demanding dullness of routine. They need, as we all do, inspirational reading and prayerful moments to recharge their spiritual batteries. But do we realize what they need most?

HELP! They need a day off. A substitute for even a few hours. They need visitors of either sex that might pitch in and help them. Instead of uttering pious nothings about God's will and how the patient's doing fine. Maybe he is, but what about the nurse? Time was when neighbors and relatives truly shared and divided works of mercy like this. Even priests, brothers, nuns felt pastoral ideals called them to clean house, do some scrubbing, assist the sick and the nurses with help on heavier tasks. Now too many are busy elsewhere, getting involved with "meaningful apostolates" that might make the headlines. Ministering to the sick, except for pay, is almost obsolete.

We forget the other purpose God has in mind in permitting moral and physical evils (so often linked with illness) in our world. We have heard about it often enough but do not like to have it hit home. God permits evils of varied types, sufferings and illnesses of all kinds—even the most baffling and heartbreaking—indeed, the followers of Jesus have abundant opportunities, rich chances to serve God and witness to Christ by ministering to the needs of our neighbors. And as the Good Samaritan story tells the whole world, our neighbor is the person who needs us, the person that next walks into our day or night needing us. That is Jesus in need. And Jesus lies there in that sickbed so you may have a chance to practice love and grow inwardly. But Jesus also stands or sits there at bedside, or bustles through that sick household doing multiple chores, in the person of the ministering nurse.

One wife recently told me of her schedule while nursing a husband dying of cancer over a six-month period after release from the hospital. Enfeebled by illness, he could just mutter garbled words and make flopping signs with his hands. So she fed him, set him up for the day, drove to work an eight-hour day, came home to be with him through the night, and then started over the next day—for weeks and unending months. Very few neighbors came and sat with him (or helped get someone who would) during the day. And on weekends nobody was around to give any relief.

The patient loved to be read to, absorbed news stories and events, was mobile enough to be taken for an automobile ride. Yet not one of his four husky, well-fixed, car-owning brothers even offered to take him for a drive. They were diligent about phoning to see how he was doing, full of good advice; later at the wake, very visible and articulate at telling people all he had been through, and what a great nurse his wife had been. They even dropped in for home visits (with one eye on their watches) with good-cheer wishes. But not one reading session, not one car ride, not even once a sitting session—so the wife might have a few hours of her own. The wife they liked, admired, praised—to other people.

Are these bad people? Or selfish or afraid? Fearful of sickness and death? Dreading their own? Devout and regular churchgoers that they were, didn't it ever cross their mind to get involved for their brother's sake? One of them said later: "His wife never asked for a relief helper. If we had known she needed help that bad, why. . . ." Sure, sure! Why must they wait for a request? What wife or anybody wants that kind of helping hand?

Do we see ourselves and our own crass negligence of people who need us in that true story? Can you multiply examples like it from your own experience? Over and over you hear of ministering-at-home nurses like that wife being isolated by devout relatives looking the other way. You can imagine how seldom any financial aid is given in such cases. I do not mean picking up the huge medical bills, although some wealthier relatives could easily do that as well. I mean just leaving twenty, fifty, a hundred dollars quietly and deftly—so maybe a little extra might be spent in the home to ease the burdens of illness.

All kinds of answers can help chronic or terminal patients and their households. Donating blood can mean much, for example. But one thing is sure, and anybody seeking to give genuine sympathy, to offer compassion or to help effectively should memorize this basic truth: The most helpful aid we can extend to afflicted, overworked people is somehow to call out their best strength that they may be able to bear the burden. Often, this is achieved best by helping them to rest and get time off to regain new drive. Our love can make us quite versatile at easing burdens for others, once we link forces with Jesus in coredeeming efforts.

Do not most of us come to realize, as we grow older, that our worst sins were those of omission? Opportunities were sent our way to help a person desperately in need—maybe a heart attack victim lying on a sidewalk—and we walked by just like the Levite in the Good Samaritan story. Perhaps there was one like the brutal police arrest of a black man which I saw and did not protest. (And I've been sorry ever since.) Perhaps it was a helpful visit to assist your family during the last hours of one of your parents —and somehow you were too busy.

We can remember hundreds of examples like those. Do they not amount to failure on our part to give a faith-response to somebody ill? Somebody suffering from loneliness, neglect, deep personal anguish, mental torment for whom we failed to come through. In our better moments we hear a refrain of "I was sick and in prison and you did not visit me. . . . What you did not do for them you did not do for me."

So often people question the mercy and goodness of a God who permits war atrocities, plagues, prenatal or postnatal defects, innocent disease victims. They might remember that God measures things by standards involving higher and longer lasting values than those we use. God never approves evil but only the good which may be drawn from it. He will not destroy man's free will, but he will turn even our sins to our salvation. And the physical evils which afflict the innocent can somehow be an untold source of goodness. Especially in terms of the good deeds of kindness, sacrifice and works of charity they call forth.

The *why* of all suffering was our opening line. Many answers are worked out in the free will choices of human beings. Yet each of us individually should ponder regularly and profoundly this "why suffer." Am I striving to be worthy of the suffering in illness that comes my way? Am I capitalizing on the rich chances sent me daily to witness to Jesus' redemption by ministering to each person in need that enters my life as someone ill in body or soul?

CHAPTER TWO

Struggles for Young Lives

> Get up, take the child and his mother with you, and
> escape into Egypt, and stay there until I tell you, because
> Herod intends to search for the child and do away with
> him.
>
> Matt. 2: 13-14

New human life battles terrible odds just to
begin, then to survive—not just to survive the many
illnesses that menace new life, but to avoid death at
the hands of adult humans. Even Jesus of David's
royal line was quickly sought out by killers. The flight
into Egypt by the Holy Family kept Herod's hired
thugs from destroying Jesus. Yet an enraged Herod
exterminated about twenty other babies under two
years of age in Bethlehem. It was a savage act typical
of the world which hates Christ whose way is life as
opposed to its way of death.

There are antilife forces today that are gaining
frightful power. All too often there seem to be per-

sons honestly concerned about giving guidance on how to live with illness. As medical people or para-medical people, they seem dedicated to services that minister to the needs of the sick. Yet the ghastly truth is that in actual practice they become peddlers of death. Anybody who seeks to help the sick must be convinced of the sacredness of life. We cannot honestly talk of ministering to patients if we actively destroy unborn life within them.

Pregnant women ordinarily are not considered sick persons. Pregnancy itself is a normal function for a woman. Yet individual women can develop patterns of physical, mental or emotional illness during pregnancy. Then we have two patients we must be aware of—the mother and the unborn child. Medical evidence indisputably maintains the fact that a fetus is a tiny independent human being, a second patient.

The most obvious position ought to be—let us do all we can for both patients to keep them well and alive. The basic tenet in the most ancient medical guideline—the Hippocratic Oath—reads: "Above all, do no harm." Who gives any human being—mother, father, doctor, nurse—the authority to decide: "This tiny patient must be put to death?" How it is done? Who wants it done? What plausible sounding reasons are given for having it done?—these are not issues. The uppermost issue remains: What human being can lawfully say to an innocent patient that he must die?

The infants killed by Herod's order are honored as martyrs. They bore witness to Jesus even though they did so without conscious knowledge. As our first chapter explained, God draws good from evil, brings blessings to humanity from innocence that suffers, grants us as adults enriching chances to minister to helpless victims of suffering. Who but God knows the beneficial results, the coredeeming values, that might come to humanity from the unborn children who some of us wildly judge should not be born?

If you are over thirty-five years of age, you have some memory of the horrors of secular science uncovered at Buchenwald and Dachau. "All for the good of Nazi society" was the diabolic defense of the extermination of millions of Jews and "problem people" like the aged, the sickly and disabled. There is a great deal of similar depravity corrupting society today. The advocates of "mercy killings" (same phrase used by Nazi doctors), genetic schemes to breed only "superior people," even committees for legalized infanticide, zealots demanding "free abortion on demand"—the ghastly horrors are back. And who shall say where they stop, once you let any mere human being be the final word on life?

In a pluralistic society like ours, fair-minded citizens do not want rules imposed from elected authorities to be taken from any one particular religious group. Look what a mess we had here in America when people who felt that any use of alcoholic beverages was wrong succeeded in inflicting prohibition on America. This chapter is not an attempt to impose upon non-Christians patterns of thought arising from Christian teachings. Neither would we judge it fair that so-called Catholic ideals about transmission of life and safeguarding unborn life be made into civil law binding all citizens.

Morality discussions about pros and cons on abortion are better left to other publications and writers. Abundant literature is already available defending reasonable changes in abortion legislation. Even more is easily available which explains in terms of divine law and fundamental ethics the conflicting rights when abortion is under discussion. What needs to be emphasized here is living with and ministering to illness humanely and kindly.

The "girl in trouble" may be an emotional wreck, close to a crackup affecting her mental health or in such bad shape physically that her baby-to-be is close to illness. We must get her and the baby—at any stage of pregnancy—the help needed so that life may be nurtured and developed to its best possibilities. How will we ever do this, if even professed followers of Christ speak of fetuses as "humanoids" and discuss casually wiping out fetuses that might be born deformed?

There are alternatives to abortion. How easy to kill off the life we do not want to bother caring for. Any pregnant woman should be offered alternatives for consideration. Good listening and wise counseling might bring about good health in mind and body for a new mother and a new baby. So often there are unfair pressures from parents, friends and/or career that crowd a pregnant woman into abortion against her own heart's choice and to her lasting regret.

So much of what passes for thoughtful pro-abortion argument is just a series of slogans, clichés and misrepresented facts. We would all do a great service for families, parishes and schools (especially young people from about fifth-grade on), to make available scientific facts about unborn children. It might amaze even Women's Lib to know.

The essential humanity of the unborn child has been established and recognized by all the modern sciences of embryology, fetology, genetics and biology. These disciplines affirm that: (1) Fetal tissue is unique. There never was nor will be another piece of tissue like it. So it is not just another part of a woman's body. (2) Fetal tissue is different from the parent organism. Ask any biologist. The chromosomes and genes of the fetus are fixed at conception and are different from those of the parents. (3) The fetus has an independent life. This is why sensible obstetricians treat the fetus as a second patient. (4) Life begins at conception and can be verified medically within fourteen days. In three weeks the fetus manifests a working heart, a nerve system and a brain different from and independent of the mother.

Maybe we need more husbands who sue for right to fatherhood. Like the prospective father in New York who won a court order preventing his estranged wife from having an abortion, destroying his flesh and blood.

Since by lawyers' expert testimony, a fetus can inherit by will, can be the beneficiary of a trust, can sue for injury, is protected from parental neglect, can have transfusions even when parents are religiously opposed so, should we not give them the right to live?

The 1970 White House Conference on Children declared that they regarded as vitally important "the right of all children to be born healthy." But as one woman physician and mother said in a letter to the *Daily News* in Chicago: "It is very difficult to be born healthy, if some doctors are being paid to cut up unborn children with curettes, poison them with salt solution, suck them out with vacuum aspirators or surgically remove them from their mothers and leave them unattended to die" (Gloria Volini Heffernan, M.D., as quoted in the *Daily News*).

How difficult some Americans make it for defective babies to be born at all or to survive after birth. The question of letting or even causing a defective child to die has been highlighted recently in *Life* magazine, news stories and prestigious scientific symposia. One infant boy died fifteen days after emerging from his mother's womb, because he was permitted to starve to death. The parents had refused to permit any surgery on the child who was born Mongoloid and with an intestinal block. The simple surgery needed so the child could be fed and live was blocked by the parents and a court decision; the hospital put the infant in a side room and a "nothing by mouth" sign on his bed—literally starved to death.

The other story blazed across America concerned a female child who is still alive. Born as a Mongoloid but with a hole in her heart and major intestinal blockage, physicians emphasized that an operation must be performed immediately or the baby would die. The mother told the hospital personnel to let the baby die. She said she had looked ahead to the life this child would lead, the hospital and heart surgery expenses, the terrific strain on her girls at home and on her own already shaky marriage and had made her decision. Her wish to allow the baby to die was not carried out. The local bureau of children's services obtained a court order and forced the intestinal operation.

Endless difficulties have piled up for the mother and family. The mother felt the state saved the baby and should keep and provide for her. Under severe emotional strain, the mother has even thought of kill-ing the child herself. She feels the decision to let a child like this die should be made and respected be-fore an attachment develops. And she feels if there were a way to quietly put the child to sleep, she would authorize it. She tends to cleaning, feeding and dress-ing the child.

Only God can sit in judgment on decisions made by parents and especially those involved in compli-cated cases like these. Yet ethical questions arising from the impact of modern technology on human life and behavior must be dealt with responsibly. We are dealing with the God-given right to life and serious conflicts involving those trying to minister to the start and continuation of new human life. The best hearts and minds among our theologians, scientists, educa-tors, medical people, lawyers should become involved in working out basic directives to guide us in involved survival problems. We should all speak loudly and clearly affirming the sacredness of human life. It is barbaric to think that "the starvation decision" was left to parents alone. What kept the state from taking over? At times we must exercise godlike powers rather than play at godlessness. The way of starvation is certainly wrong.

A great many theologians have taught us for centuries that we are not obliged to take extraordinary measures (including tremendous bills and extremely complicated medical techniques) to keep life going. So why did a social agency force a decision upon the parents of the second child, after they had chosen not to take extraordinary means? To have given that child all the supportive therapy—yet stop short of major surgery—would have been a morally defensible position. If the state chose to take a different position—perhaps even through a court order—then let the state provide. The parents would have been within their basic rights of conscience by not bringing the child home to live.

"Every physician develops his own ethical attitude," commented Dr. Reuben Matalon, a scholar of the Joseph P. Kennedy Foundation for the Mentally Retarded, concerning the news accounts. "My own attitude is to give the baby the support it needs. If it needs antibiotics or blood or other supportive therapy, these should be provided. If the infant is extremely defective, I would give it simple care but not extraordinary care, such as a major operation, because there is nothing you can do."

Many pediatricians (the doctors who take over the newborn's care after delivery) feel that difficult decisions should not fall on the doctors or parents alone but rather on society. "A judge would provide the ruling of society, said Dr. Robert Mendelsohn, University of Illinois professor of pediatrics. "Difficult decisions should be submitted to an appropriate court."

And a very compassionate approach about the feelings of the mother who is left with the badly handicapped child was given by another pediatrician. Dr. Herbert Grossman, Director of the Illinois State Pediatric Institute said: "It is not enough to conclude that a Mongoloid child should be given every chance at life. . . . There must be a greater effort on the part of society to accept these problems as community problems and provide a greater array of resources.

Most parents of Mongoloids feel so much alone. The worst thing one can do is to leave them on their own."

The rights to life and to dignity in dying will recur frequently in this book. Here we might pause to remind readers how easily basic ethical principles can be confusedly written up in news stories. Words like "mercy killing" and "euthanasia" are tossed off glibly in highly emotional discussions. Our well-intentioned sympathies can go badly awry. Our willingness to judge another human being and project what we would have done easily leads us into false statements. That is why we all need to develop compassion (that tender virtue that feels and hopes to ease somehow the pain of other people). And compassion is kind but not gushy. It sees that lasting moral values must be understood and applied to the best of our ability, even while our hearts ache for others.

Take the word *euthanasia* that is so often made to sound peaceful and merciful. To be sure, in Greek it means "good death" and we easily use it to mean "painless death." But good dictionaries and medical texts remind us that it is the *action* of inducing the painless death of a person for reasons assumed to be merciful (to paraphrase a few good sources). We are dealing with *direct action* that terminates life. We thus move into areas involving direct killing, homicide, murder, suicide. Not nearly such pretty words as painless, merciful, sleeping away.

So whether a theologian or a scientist talks of euthanasia, he is talking about putting somebody to death. That is quite different from "letting somebody die" as the result of an infirmity. Euthanasia remains a direct act of killing, no matter how well-intentioned the "trigger man" and it will always be morally wrong. Even when the patient begs you to take his life. He cannot morally justify his suicide nor you his murder. That needs to be well-understood in our antilife society. It is quite different from keeping a person alive by extraordinary means. We can suspend those measures or refuse to continue them and be morally blameless.

Sometimes people visit our mentally retarded patients—perhaps five to twelve in mental age, but as

high as forty in calendar age—and they question us.
"Sure, each child has a right to life and should be
given ordinary helps that nurse life along, and leave
the rest in God's hands. But don't you think, Father,
that some babies have a right not to be born?
Wouldn't it have been better had many of these not
been born?"

Better for whom? And in what way should we
have arranged that they not be born? And what
agency or relative or friend presumes to make a decision that must be faced primarily by parents. Talk
to parents who chose to share life even with "fringe
kids" like these. Share some moments with the MRs,
as we call them in distinction to MIs, those who are
mentally ill. Each of us has to overcome some hidden hostility we have toward the handicapped. Too
often we do not like looking at or dealing with them,
because we are so vividly reminded of our own
limitations.

Retarded children form the largest single bloc in
the whole group of handicapped children. That's

43

right, the largest single bloc. There are more retarded children than all the children suffering blindness, deafness, and orthopedic disabilities put together. Yet so often they are caught in an educational and social no-man's land. They often languish in ordinary classrooms (harmful to them and to the classes), or stagnate at home. Yet they have a natural, democratic, Christian right to educational programs adapted to their limited disabilities. Five percent of our country's six million retardates are "hidden away" in institutions. Ninety-five percent are "hidden" in the broad daylight of our parishes. Most remain uninstructed in religion, though about seventy-five percent are only mildly retarded and are certainly educable enough to make First Communion. But many never have, because our parishes are not truly aware of them.

The current publicity program sponsored by several national organizations to help the mentally retarded focuses on this sentence: "President John Kennedy helped five and one half million retarded children. Have you helped even one?" That would be a good question for each of us to ask in terms of help given to families with retarded children, and especially in regard to helping the children receive instruction.

If parents were encouraged by parishes and schools to make known to priests and teachers that their children are retarded, they would do so. They want and need help, but they know how often so many of us just look the other way. Teaching materials and programs can be searched out, if once we try helping this segment of God's People who need and deserve special spiritual care.

As late as 1962, no mentally retarded person had worked for the Federal Government. President Kennedy took a first step, hiring a young upholsterer to work in the White House. Other officials followed: Civil Service encouraged the policy. Now more than six thousand mentally retarded are employed by departments of the Federal Government.

There is great new hope for the mentally retarded these days. We can test for PKU and control it by diet. We can vaccinate against measles, and even against German measles. We are tracking down causes of Mongolism. And we now know that seventy-five percent of all mental retardation is found among the poor where birth defects go undetected. So we can work to alleviate the causes of retardation —bad education, parental ignorance, poor diet, and lack of medical care.

Mrs. Rose Kennedy has given our whole nation an object lesson in what can be done to help. The Flame of Hope Candles and the Special Olympics have shown how much retardates can accomplish, if given chances for accomplishment. Our lives and theirs are enriched by shared love.

CHAPTER THREE

Illness and Separation

> Three days later, they found him in the Temple . . . They
> were overcome when they saw him and his mother said
> to him: "My child, why have you done this to us? See
> how worried your father and I have been, looking for
> you." "Why were you looking for me?" he replied. "Did
> you not know that I must be busy with my Father's
> affairs?" But they did not understand what he meant.
>
> Luke 2: 46-50

So often we do not understand what God
means, especially when illness or suffering becomes
a separating force in a family. Yet see how at this
moment the sword of renunciation brought Joseph
and Mary into greater unity with Jesus. In the events
following this episode, however, Joseph will slip out
of the Gospel story because Jesus in his public life
will be entirely dedicated to his Father's business and
no family ties will interfere. Mary will continue

deeply involved with Jesus, but no longer just as wife of Joseph the Carpenter and mother of a boy Jesus. In the role God plans for her—first of all believers and exemplar for all Christians—Mary will find fulfillment. Mary's destiny, foretold years ago by Simeon, comes home deeply in this separation sorrow.

Even though separation brought anguish, it brought closeness to Christ and Christians. For both Joseph and Mary came to know mental and emotional pains, even as Jesus would all through his Passion. They were sharing with Jesus as coredeemers. Mary especially endured her agony in the garden, her Gethsemane. Even as Jesus knew mental anguish as he sweated drops of blood, Mary knew a deep anguish in this loss, this discovery, this bafflement. The first believer and exemplar for us must personally experience what so many of us suffer from separation arising from illness. Then she will indeed be a Refuge of Sinners.

Think of the first agonizing moments for family members when it becomes known that the newborn

baby is physically defective or mentally damaged—
the rush of tender protection, the feeling of how
much love we will give to heal, but also the pain of
separation. This child is different, not like the rest of
the family. Will people outside hurt him? Ridicule
him? Even resent him? Can we keep him with us
always or will he have to be put in an institution?
What medical care does he need right now? How will
we ever pay for it all? What is God asking? What
does he mean?

And we think of Joseph and Mary: "They did not
understand what he meant." So we ponder and pray
and rethink our values and priorities. Only parents
and devoted relatives who have lived through such
pain can tell its whole story. Yet somehow so many
of them we have all known do find values to sustain
them, motives to strengthen them, power through
God's loving help to toil with love they never dreamed
possible.

Perhaps the first thing we all need to do in the face
of such a separating kind of pain is to remember:

This afflicted one is God's child loaned to us. We must always honor his human dignity and possibilities for sharing divine happiness. Our perspective must be truly Christian, imitative of Christ. The redeeming value of all suffering must become for us a truth that inspires and comforts us. It is never easy to accept and live with crippling handicaps and mental sufferings, to bear patiently the loneliness they bring to patients and those ministering to them. But as our insight deepens, we grow in awareness of how close to Jesus agonizing in the Garden and Mary suffering her three-day loss are those who suffer such illness or separation.

We hope and pray that such values and motives will influence us. Each human being brings his own response to handicaps affecting the relationships of mind and body. There is the worry of how far the physical limitations will throw off the mental functions and the deeper worry that even when the child learns to live with his physical limitations, will his brain still be so damaged or off-balance that he will need long stretches of hospitalization or perhaps years of institutional life.

Mental health problems form the number one health problem for America. One out of every ten families does or will deal with its presence among their loved ones. Do not let Pollyanna speeches and articles lead you to believe that the rush-to-release programs so widespread in our country have notably diminished the gravity of the problem. Too often the releasing of patients not yet ready to live safely in a complex society with complex ailments is a disaster. The patients come back sicker than ever to public hospitals. There is grave suspicion surrounding such rush programs, suspicion of emphasizing statistics and treating humans like animals, perhaps even exploiting them for profit.

Let newspapers conduct exposé investigations; let legislatures make more detailed plans for patients instead of buildings; let the families use the political influence of votes to obtain better and more humane treatment of emotionally or mentally troubled patients.

This is not a crusade handbook. It is a series of thoughtful reminders to help us become followers with Christlike ideals toward all sick people. Perhaps no other group needs our Christlike understanding as much as those who suffer physical, emotional and mental ailments. Our society still avoids, stigmatizes and neglects them.

You might think things out along three levels: First, dealing with these illnesses that separate, that is, that make a family member different and special, in your own family setup. Second, dealing with them through an institutional setting. Third, dealing with them once the patient returns home for what might be a lengthy or permanent stay. At all three levels we should try to help patients see what they have in their favor, what they have going for them, rather than burden them with anxieties about what they lack physically, emotionally or mentally.

This is one reason why it is such a fine idea to publicize names like the Joseph Kennedy School for *Exceptional* Children. A touch like that can make thousands realize how special in God's eyes are the brave cross-bearers, how deeply tender is the indwelling of God in such souls.

At all times we should get accurate medical help for our patients. Parishes, schools, families and community groups can and should be enlisted to help us. Emotional, nervous, organic or mental problems—or some combination of these—are not to be treated lightly or laughed off as "oddball." They involve genuine mental suffering. The pain is real. If we see Christ in each sick person, we will find ways to give help. So, if you can, do get help and decide to keep your patient at home.

Perhaps you keep the patient home because you received no help or just could not get your loved one into a hospital setting. Take the lead-poisoned children who are so badly ignored in our ghetto areas. Each year, nationwide, about 400,000 youngsters are infected, half of them ending up with permanent handicaps or impaired intellectual ability. It is an accepted medical truism that mental illness is more prevalent among the poor, because for them the usual pathways to detection and treatment are blocked by such things as overcrowding, unemployment, discrimination, hunger and the other consequences of poverty.

If we ran a check on homes with a sick person enduring mental anguish, we would discover things like epilepsy, polio, mental retardation from injuries, minds damaged before or at birth, possibly deepseated neurosis or even serious psychosis. These ailments will involve persons of various calendar ages and various mental ages. Consider first what we might get across to the patients. Then, think how those ministering can be encouraged, how they can help themselves, and how we can help them. And "we" means each one of us who encounters such illness.

What we must try to bring home to patients—allowing for their limitations—is that God loves them

dearly and personally. Through their suffering they
can witness Christ's redemption to people around
them. Never must we allow somebody we love, even
though he is seemingly so much separated from us
mentally, to feel that his life is a burden to the family,
that it is a life without purpose, or that he gives nothing to those who care for him. The truth is that he is
sharing for us the redeeming sufferings of Christ.

People who enjoy full health often object that a
mentally ill person really cannot witness like this,
since he has not chosen his vocation of suffering and
usually is not reconciled to it. All the more reason
why we must labor to help him be *able* to *accept* his
suffering, so that he may better come to terms with
it, better understand his deepest communion with
Christ. Even tell him that Christ as a man, and he
really was a man, did not *choose* his passion. He
accepted it: "If it be possible, let this chalice pass me
by: only as thy will is, not as mine is."

How often have you heard medical people talk of
TLC (tender loving care) as the greatest medicine.
Make sure your patient receives loads of it daily.

Every service you render can convey it. But above all, tell him you need him, that he is helping all of us in our witness to Christ.

"Many a retardate has been disowned by his physical father. Many more have never acquired a spiritual one. The progenitors of mentally deficient offspring often want them to "get lost." Their pastors more often just do not "find" them. It seems to me that the easiest and surest way to be aware of retarded parishioners is to ask the question—from the pulpit or in the Sunday bulletin.

"Tell us. We want to know. We care."

This observation by a Catholic Chaplain for Newark State School in New York emphasizes a direct method of bringing Christ to the retarded (and it could mean others emotionally or mentally ill) in every parish. How many families have suffered untold misery, because "Father doesn't care." Since three percent of our population is mentally retarded, there is a good possibility that every parish has a number of such patients who are educable and can be helped into fuller sacramental life. Stop to think what marvelous work could be done by nuns, seminarians, catechists, and parish groups looking for new apostolates.

It has always amazed me while traveling as a missionary to see so many splendid husbands and fathers in parishes giving such importance to athletic programs. Think what could be done by such groups— even while helping the sports program—in terms of home visits where sick patients need attentive visitors. Look what the Kennedy family did with Special Olympics nationally for "exceptional" children.

There is still too much "stigma" attached to illnesses that separate—especially mental illness. Think how enriching for patients and families it could be if more of us saw such illness as *stigmata* (wounds of Christ?) Then we would head off this hiding in shame from the neighbors, relatives, even ourselves the truth about illnesses. There should be no shame attached to being sick in mind or body. Our still primitive aversion to any psychiatric checkups causes thousands of tragedies a year. So when something is really wrong with a relative's mental state, get him to sign in for hospital treatment.

Yet do not feel disappointed that all may not go too well at the hospital. Institutional treatment of the mentally ill is badly in need of overhaul across America. But when a home situation has become too much to handle, and there is danger from the patient's erratic or maybe irrational behavior (danger to himself or others and even criminal acts in the offing), family members must at least get custodial care for the sick one. Once the patient is there, many things can be done to make his stay helpful. Kindness, visits, cooperation with hospital personnel, working with the chaplain of the proper faith—all are basic steps to take.

A group of 100 ex-mental patients, calling themselves Mental Patients Liberation Project, have declared war on the entire U.S. mental hospital system. Outraged by the abuse and ill-treatment they have suffered and seen others suffer in institutions, they are demanding full and unequivocal rights. Here are some of their demands:

(1) Abolition of forced or involuntary commitment to mental hospitals (only a crime or overt antisocial act should cause such entry). (2) An end to treatment and medication without the patient's consent (they know proper medication can be arbitrated). (3) The right to leave the institution when the patient wants (they realize sensible restraint makes sense). (4) Full rights as citizens and human beings inside the hospitals. (5) The establishment of neighborhood "crisis centers" run by ex-patients, to provide emergency refuge and guidance to troubled people in need of help. According to MPLP, which operates from a storefront at 56 E. 4th Street in New York City, the need for change extends to both private and public mental institutions.

This group may do for mental patients what was done long ago for problem drinkers by *Alcoholics*

Anonymous. Even a small beginning should be encouraged in our earnest efforts to be truly humane and genuinely Christian. The degrading abuses decried by this group include oversedating patients, using them as guinea pigs by giving untried and experimental drugs, degrading them and mocking them by cruel punishments. All are too often true and widespread. As one of their members said at a MPLP meeting: "Most people are unaware of what is going on in our mental hospitals. If every American were incarcerated in a mental institution for a week, there would be changes made."

We all should try to help progressive efforts to improve the lot of patients in our mental hospitals. Despite serious abuses that need correcting—and we can channel our protests through public officials, elected representatives, news media—many good programs exist that we can aid. Volunteer workers and visitors are still very much in demand and do immense good for patients. Yet it is sad to notice how seldom Catholic parishes or Catholic diocesan organizations are represented. Maybe spiritual leaders have not fought hard enough to overcome that "stigma" attitude toward troubled-in-mind patients.

With long-term patients—mostly geriatric types, patients very much out of reality, badly retarded patients or badly infirm types—visits by relatives and volunteer groups should have highest priority. Do not be afraid. Most sick people are as gentle as little children, and just as lonely for affection, notice and attention. "For of such is the kingdom of heaven," said Jesus. Would you try to do what he would do? Even mentally ill people have cycles of in-contact or out-of-contact. The "lucid intervals" might surprise and delight you, as you discover that troubled people have learned so much and can teach so much.

What about dealing with patients who return home? This might come about by a transition through a "halfway house" or "sheltered care" house. These are used as means to gradually restore patients to community or home living. If only our communities would get more involved in mental health programs and families would assist community agencies more, then the transition would be successful. Institutional living usually will do just so much good for patients; then it is a downhill process. So releasing large numbers of patients to work them gradually into communities or homes has great merit. It follows splendid theory but right now it is being badly executed.

Once more we need individuals and families using channels of protest for suitable social changes—political, legislative, news media. And we need people like our readers to be Christlike in behavior—visit the sick and lonely. Do what Catholics in Gheel, Belgium, have done for centuries with immense success. Bring former patients into your home as guests or as domestic help, paying them (please God) a decent wage. The gentle tone of a friendly household does wonders for troubled minds—minds hurt for years by lack of understanding kindness and individual treatment.

With liberal rules from Bishops and the Holy See these days, we might even see parishes arranging for

religious or laymen to bring Holy Communion to patients in these badly ignored halfway houses. The
rules were liberalized so priests could have more help
on such tasks.

Suppose your relative-patient comes back home to
you, what about your patterns of behavior? With
those who are physically handicapped or mentally
retarded, you have a fairly predictable level of behavior to handle. You know from experience or the
hospital personnel can guide you. You also are fairly
well aware of intellectual limitations. Learning abili-
ties reach a certain level you can count on—and perhaps raise.

What about a mental patient returning home? Try
to realize that he needs understanding kindness and
not pity or self-indulgence. Mostly he needs to be
treated as recovered from his illness. We do not need
to go into the different types of neuroses or psychoses
to be aware that every human being responds to
naturalness. So treat the returnee as you would treat
anyone else in your home. Let him talk or not talk

about his hospital stay and its results. Usually he would like to forget it. Often he will give you laughs, recalling the humor in it all. That's great; seeing humor that way is an excellent sign of returned mental health.

It is not vital to most of us as nonprofessionals to judge a "cure" of a psychosis. It is debatable if anybody is totally "cured" of what a mental illness does to a personality. Rejoice that the sick person is home, recovered, stabilized and happy to be in loving surroundings. You would violate politeness by staring at a scar left from physical injury in a patient. Then, do not stare at his possible psychic scars.

We often say to our departing patients: "God bless you. Stay well. And I hope I don't see you around here again." The smile eases things. Maybe after-care programs will help greatly. My favorite is called *Recovery, Inc.*—its address and phone number is in most city directories. All Christ asked of his apostles at Gethsemane was to be there. Be there with the one suffering mental anguish, trusting your love and God's to keep him well.

CHAPTER FOUR

Behavior Crosses

> As they were leading him away they seized on a man,
> Simon from Cyrene . . . and made him shoulder the cross.
> . . . Large numbers of people followed him, and women
> too, who mourned and lamented for him.
>
> Luke 23 : 26-28

The *Stations of the Cross* have been a popu-
lar devotion with followers of Christ since the thir-
teenth century. The sad events they present for our
meditation are consistent with the four Gospels. Even
though we have no explicit text which says that Mary
met Jesus carrying his cross to Calvary, the text given
above makes quite plausible the pious assumption
that such a meeting may have happened.

There was a well-established Talmudic tradition of
noblewomen practicing merciful kindness by accom-
panying condemned criminals to render them chari-
table services. These are probably the women referred

to here, and to them Jesus uttered his prophetic reminder that they should weep for themselves more than for him (a clear reference to the awful destruction of Jerusalem coming later).

The Fourth Station of the *Way of the Cross* and our own Servite *Way of the Mother* calls upon us to contemplate in mind and heart the anguish sustained by Mary as she meets Jesus along the Way of Calvary. As the great Dominican theologian Edward Schillebeeckx emphasizes for us: "Mary knows what it is to suffer as a human being. . . . A grown-up son is still his mother's boy. . . . He never ceases to be her child. How can we then imagine Mary's human agony when her child met her on the Way to Calvary and later, when she saw him, her divine child, die upon the Cross?" (*Mary, Mother of Redemption.* Sheed and Ward.)

Crucifixion was a degrading spectacle from start to finish. The condemned person, stripped naked and beaten along with whips, was forced to carry the heavy crossbar on his shoulders. The upright of the cross was already permanently fixed at the place of execution. It is easy to see why that crossbar was too much for Jesus in his weakened condition, and also to see why the bullying Romans would force a chance passerby to take up the burden. Yet what a blessing came to Simon of Cyrene—to be a relief crossbearer for Jesus.

So the Fifth Station of the Cross which we have pondered so often makes good sense in light of the Gospel narrative. In this very sick society in which we struggle to overcome man's monstrous behavior to other men, it makes sense for us to meditate again upon the Way of the Cross, and not just during Holy Week, but frequently, especially in our struggle to bear illness or minister to illness.

This chapter will deal with what we might call Behavior Crosses. We endure within ourselves, from others or in company with others, these illnesses which stem from flaws in our damaged human natures. They might include alcoholism, drug addiction, obsessive gambling, violent emotional behavior or sexually deviant behavior. The findings of depth psychology have given us greater understanding of the *why* beneath patterns of bizarre behavior. The *what* and the *how* are highlighted every day in the various news media and communications. Troubles within ourselves and our families must be dealt with as crosses which we cause ourselves and others; they must be accepted and borne bravely knowing that dealing with pain, our own and that of others, forms a big part in our sharing Christ's redemption.

Simon of Cryrene did not ask for that relief cross-bearer role which so transformed his life and immortalized him. Just as battered children do not ask to be born of seriously ill and sadistic parents. The many friends and the compassionate women following Jesus step by agonizing step to Calvary were quite helpless against "the system" that had condemned him and was now executing him. Just as loving parents, families and friends feel so helpless to combat the miserable social conditions in our society that entrap promising youngsters into fatal drug habits. If God would permit the Mother of Redemption to be so deeply "involved" in the bloody gruesomeness of the crucifixion, who are we to question God's ways of permitting "sick people" to bring their every little burden to us?

Why do the troubled emotional lives and twisted minds of people harass us? How do we find strength to cope with crosses? What rich human growth in being Christlike can be ours with proper acceptance? These are things which we will clarify in terms of the values and priorities that we hold uppermost. If our top priority becomes "law and order" at all costs, even at the cost of sacrificing justice, mercy and loving our neighbor, then we will ravage our prey in this jungle society worse than the sickest of those we condemn in our righteous indignation.

But if we honestly and earnestly ask ourselves how we can strive to see things as Christ saw them, if we cooperate with the ideals which Christ taught as Mary did, we could take steps—and they might seem quite small—to heal many ill persons. We can help ourselves and them, even amid our many ups and downs, to share with Christ the ongoing work of redeeming this world. Christ still comes to us in the person of a junkie, an alkie, a nympho, all asking for our compassionate love.

It probably took Simon of Cyrene long months and years to realize the riches he won that day by helping out a condemned criminal. Those devout Jewish women, so faithful to their tradition of mercy toward the condemned, probably came to great rejoicing later, in knowing they had ministered to the long-promised Messiah. And people like you and I? How amazed and grateful we will be, as life's prudent way of "don't be a sucker" falls away before eternity's reality of "what you did for the least of these you did for me."

In a lecture in Chicago, the great-hearted Gilbert K. Chesterton once explained: "Loving means to love that which is unlovable—or it is no virtue at all. Forgiving means to pardon the unpardonable—or it is no virtue at all. Faith means believing the unbelievable—or it is no virtue at all. And to hope means hoping when things are hopeless—or it is no virtue at all."

Take the social problem known as "Battered Child Syndrome." We read or hear stories about an infant's flesh being burned with cigarettes, a baby immersed in a sink of scalding water or a baby's bones broken. We murmur: "What kind of pathetic parents do thinks like these? Thank God we never did anything like that." It is so easy to grow indignant at child abuse. How seldom do we try to understand the illness at work? This behavior that is so shocking stems from the illness. Suppose it were at work within you or someone close to you? What would be done then?

We could start by trying to understand what medical scientists have discovered about this problem. One characteristic child abusers have in common is this: As children, they had been abused themselves, either physically or emotionally. They had lived through continuous demand from parents, constant parental criticism. No matter what the child tried to do, it was not enough; it was not right; it bothered the parents or disgraced them before others.

When children are so pushed around, the pattern repeats itself when they grow up and have their own children. Deprived of parental love in their infancy, they look to their own children for what they missed. You can almost take for granted that each child abuser is convinced that infants and children exist primarily to satisfy parental needs. To them the children's needs are unimportant and should be disregarded. Children who do not fulfill their requirements simply deserve punishment.

One child abuser admitted to a medical investigator: "I have never felt really loved all my life. When the baby was born, I thought he would love me. When he cried, it meant he didn't love me. So I hit him."

Sure, all fifty states have child-abuse statutes on their books. Likewise, they have laws against other behavior illnesses such as gambling which is compulsive, drinking which is alcoholism and using drugs because of addiction. But legal action against child abusers seldom does much good. Such pressure reinforces their conviction that "I'm always being disregarded, attacked, commanded to do better." The very things which led them to be child abusers.

Medical records so often show that child abusers seem on the surface to be "normal" persons. Only a few will show up as overtly psychotic, victims of drugs or alcohol, or mentally retarded. So it seems that such jolting behavior stems from emotional wounds sustained in their own traumatic childhood. What can be done to help break the chain?

Since 1937 our troubled world has gained inestimable knowledge about sick behavior from organizations such as *Alcoholics Anonymous*. In California, a new group with over 60 members has been formed called *Mothers Anonymous*. Imitating the group therapy methods of the reformed drinkers who always speak of *arresting* their sickness of alcoholism by not taking the first drink—and helping each other get through one day at a time—these mothers strive to reduce child abuse and build up the parent's self-image. Their methods are working—even in cases where jail terms or private psychiatric therapy had not helped. It does seem that they will need professional guidance, counseling and the help only to be found in religion. But their work should spread for it is based on good sense. Sick people can help each other. The organization has its headquarters in Redondo Beach, California.

Far more widespread, more likely to touch our lives personally, or one of our family members, is the sickness of alcoholism. Despite the world-wide publicity given to *Alcoholics Anonymous* and its admitted success (far surpassing any other means on record in *arrested* cases), this way of life still needs to be better known and understood. Often the people needing its help most—perhaps one of us social drinkers—ridicule it as "do good-ism" or refer to it as "those killjoy reformers."

Our major addiction problem in the United States is not heroin. It is alcohol. Governmental agencies,

medical authorities and all people who deal with behavior problems stemming from drug abuse agree on
this. Liquor is more dangerous than all other drugs
put together. The National Council on Alcoholism
estimates there are nine million—"and that's a rock-
bottom statistic"—nine million alcoholics, desperately ill people in the United States. If alcoholism
were a communicable disease, such as diphtheria or
smallpox, a national emergency would be declared.
Perhaps as high as five percent of our population is
addicted to alcohol. Thirty-eight percent of all police
arrests involve drunkenness. Sixty percent of fatal
traffic accidents involve drinkers. One in ten male
alcoholics commits suicide—and women come close
to that.

The nearest telephone directory lists a phone number for your local *Alcoholics Anonymous* group.
These acknowledged experts are dedicated people
and they are helping themselves stay dry by helping
others stay dry. Their famous Twelve Steps are a
group of principles, spiritual in nature, which, if prac-

ticed as a way of life, can expel the obsession for alcohol and enable the sufferer to become a happy and whole person useful to family, community, society.

Abundant literature has been published, catalogued, made easily available to drinkers and non-drinkers alike through the worldwide apostolate of the recovery of alcoholics. The major difficulty is to get people to read, digest, strive to spread the truth about this drug problem. This is especially difficult when the problem is your own. Second only to that is getting your married partner or a close relative to face the truth about problem drinking that so quickly becomes alcoholism.

Just as drug-prone young people listen most and profit best from testimonials of *arrested* junkies their own age and with whom they are acquainted, so most of us social drinkers learn best from *recovered* alcoholics our age whom we know.

In your own family circle there are wonderful chances to impress youngsters that this disease can trap them. The vast majority of our teen-agers who have serious behavior problems come from alcoholic homes. Again, how can we help break the chain? A beginning is to tell the truth to youngsters—in school, in church-related teachings, community programs and youth counseling projects. Diabetics cannot eat like other people. Alcoholics cannot drink like other people. We can detect signs of diabetes and also alcoholism. Factors are known and can be detected that make some of us highly susceptible to this illness. We should do all we can to spread such valuable help.

But how do you live with the alcoholic person, the person you love, wish to help, yet know as a stubbornly determined drinker? His self-inflicted illness is clearer to him than any other love. Even the Chancery Office might advise you to separate or hospitalize your partner. The illness could worsen into brain damage syndrome resulting in insanity or even death. So many versions of this illness can be chronicled, but one thing is certain: Nobody is ever hopeless. Many people are helpless. Each one of us—as chances come our way—must minister as a Christian to the needs of every alcoholic. Probe your own conscience. God will judge us there. Do not be so afraid of "being taken in" by alkies. Risk being a fool for Christ's sake!

Since abuse of alcohol is our number one drug problem, all we have learned about dealing with it should be used to combat other drug abuses. Yet we never seem to learn. Prohibition in America led to the utter corruption of public life and the widespread success of gangsterism. This happened because we insisted upon making a moral and legal problem out of what is basically a behavior and illness problem. And again today, we persist in doing just that with narcotics. We worry endlessly about how to cut the supplies of the one percent of our population hooked on drugs. We do next to nothing about the millionaire pushers who wax fat on the sick addicts, while our crime rate which menaces ninety-nine percent of our population continues to rise astronomically.

We need to give something like methadone or even hard drugs to addicts in the same way we give insulin to diabetics. A drug addict is almost never dangerous when under the influence for narcotics are sedatives. What makes him terribly dangerous to society is the desperate need for money to buy the next dose. He must steal up to three hundred dollars a day to support his habit for which he would do *anything*.

Does he commit these criminal acts because he is evil or corrupt? He pursues them because he is carrying a behavior cross ("the monkey on his back") which stems from illness. He is sick and he needs a doctor's care; he needs loving compassion, even as he drives himself toward utter destruction. How probingly will Jesus some day judge hypocrites in high and safe places who have enriched themselves helping "pushers" and killing "junkies."

Do we eliminate pushers and criminal seduction and hypocritical laws by jailing or hospitalizing addicts? Most psychiatrists have given up on the problem. Federal narcotics hospitals will not boast of even ten percent "cure" results—more than likely it is closer to two percent. The organized crime groups oppose reform of narcotics laws, just as the bootleggers fought the repeal of prohibition. We'll have addiction problems as long as we have human beings. But we could be honest and realistic in helping those who are sick.

Imagine what protests you would receive for suggesting that we make drugs easier to get for sick people; then, think what you would hear for suggesting that we legalize all forms of gambling! Once again you will find powerful forces—organized crime and those it can buy and corrupt—determined to keep things as they are. But the greatest contributors to the skyhigh profits of gambling are sick people. That's right, sick with the compulsion to gamble. America has been slower to learn of this kind of compulsion than that of alcoholism. Yet it is a behavior cross as old as humanity, as common a sickness as drug addiction and as destructive of individuals and families as suicide or murder.

Fortunately there is *Gamblers Anonymous* to help the afflicted for there are very few other sources of help. Aside from the strength of will developed by a healthy spiritual life, religion is not the answer. We are dealing with a compulsion which involves emotional illness. The *desire* to gamble never leaves this kind of person. But the act of gambling can be *arrested*. Much like the first step in the *Alcoholics Anonymous* program, the Recovery Program for Gamblers demands a difficult act of humility. The gambler must admit to himself that he is a *compulsive* gambler and that he is *powerless* to stop betting on his own.

The GA program is patterned quite closely upon the AA program. The philosophy is much the same, including the constant need for help from a higher Power. There is strong emphasis upon group therapy and crisis intervention (calling upon a member when the temptation is great). The handbook and literature available to people seeking help can be obtained through more than one hundred chapters scattered across our land. The national headquarters for this nonsectarian, self-supporting fellowship is in Los Angeles. Detailed information can be had by writing

Gamblers Anonymous, P.O. Box 17173, Los Angeles, 90017.

Very puzzling for those who have never experienced this compulsion is the reason why these people gamble. "We gamble for the thrill, not the amount involved. If we won all the money in the world, we would be back the next day looking for new action. When you're like us, you've got to lose it all back," is a typical confession at a group meeting.

The GA handbook agrees with the findings of medical men that compulsive gambling is due to: *Inability* and *unwillingness* to accept reality, followed by an escape into a dream world of fantasy. *Emotional insecurity* and a sense of not belonging. *Immaturity* accompanied by a desire to avoid responsibility. This finally becomes a subconscious obsession. In addition to these causes, many psychiatrists say that the subconscious desire to lose is a form of masochism, close to perverse sexual gratification.

We must try to understand for ourselves and for those we seek to help that behavior crosses cause genuine pain. They stem from causes often hidden from the victim of compulsion, even more hidden from their families and friends. Our prayers, our compassion and our self-sacrifice, putting forth that little extra effort to help someone struggling—these are priceless. The group therapy programs which we have indicated have wrought wonders for thousands of troubled people. Yet they all believe their good results can double, when families and friends accompany them to meetings, encourage them and bear with their ups and downs. Don't give up loving them.

CHAPTER FIVE

Lessons in Dying

> See his mother and the disciples he loved standing near her, Jesus said to his mother, "Woman, this is your son." Then to the disciples he said, "This is your mother." And from that moment the disciple made a place for her in his home.
>
> John 19: 26-27

John actually saw and heard the scene described above. Many theologians have called it "The Cross Annunciation." They remind us that the Annunciation recorded by Luke (1: 26-38) was a message from God to Mary through the angel Gabriel; but this Annunciation is a message to Mary from God through his Son. A message the whole world should hear and strive to understand for it is a proclamation of Mary's spiritual motherhood of the redeemed as the New Eve, the mother of the living, a symbol of the church. She is given as her son the beloved disciple who exemplifies the perfect Christian. Mary is

85

given by Jesus the commission of a mother caring for those who would follow him.

With this commission to his mother, Jesus had finished the work he came to do. A few moments later, he bowed his head and gave up his spirit. We should treasure the last words of men about to die, as Mary and John long remembered the commission given them by Jesus. It was almost as if he had said: "I am about to die; Joseph is already dead; here is your new family. Mary, Mother of the Redeemer, be you now and forever Mother of the Redeemed."

If we are to live with illness and minister to illness as God intended, how much we need to know, love, imitate, win help and guidance from the New Eve, Mother of the Redeemed. Above all we need Mary's example and influence to learn lessons in dying.

Go back mentally to Calvary on Good Friday. Jesus Redeemer is being nailed to a cross, one of the cruelest forms of execution devised by man. And John tells us that Mary "stood" near that cross. The word "stood" implies the posture of a brave woman.

There was no fainting, no fleeing, only compassionate sharing. Here indeed was death with dignity and
ministering with dedication.

Mary was totally absorbed in three tasks during
those agonizing hours. She was listening. She was
sharing. She was learning. The very three tasks that
should engross us all when caring for the dying. Like
Jesus, those who face illness which leads to death
have very important things to tell us. Letting them
speak and really hearing what they say can often be
our greatest gift to them before they leave us. And
if we do truly listen, we shall be led to genuine sharing. How could we cruelly turn from their need to
assuage aloneness? Most certainly, listening and
sharing will bring us rich learning—lessons we will
use for the rest of our lives and on through our own
dying.

It is true that Jesus had come to terms with all that
his dying would demand of him long before Calvary.
His prayerful acceptance in the Garden of Gethsemane climaxed a life of willing what his Father willed.

He had no thought or hope of a remittance, a turning back, a relief from the agony—as we often have and must have with our dying. There was indeed his awareness of the coming triumph of Resurrection. Yet in human terms—indeed Jesus was intensely human—all that was blanked out. He was alone with agonizing suffering, except for the compassionate sharing of Mary and his loyal friends.

Allowing for that difference—and similar differences which we learn through meditation—we can see and hear in our dying patients all that took place on Calvary. Since our patients are coredeeming in union with Jesus—they are Jesus in our midst—we must strive to be like Mary to them. She listened, she shared, she learned—so must we.

So many of us talk too much, try to be busy—busy too much, and do not listen. Even when a patient is almost crying out: "Will you please talk with me; answer my questions; don't run off"—we don't pause to really hear. They need to talk about their fears and their aloneness. Try to realize that, except for unusually intelligent and well-motivated people, the dying person seldom believes this death business can really happen to him. So he has to contend with fear, trepidation, anguish, even despair. These are natural and instinctual attitudes. Even the best theological approach will not wipe them out, but a faith-inspired attitude may rechannel them.

Where will the patient and those caring for him acquire such a faith-inspired attitude—the kind this whole book is a plea for? We will find it in prayerful thought about suffering and death, family awareness and sharing of experiences with the dying, proper training in schools by clergy, teachers and medical people. Within the past decade there has been an immense effort to improve care for the dying. Books and articles about dying with dignity and ways to achieve a peaceful death increase daily. The long-taboo subject in America is now widely treated in colleges, seminaries and medical schools. We have such a long way to go that we should eagerly share the little knowledge we do possess.

Every day more than 5,000 patients die. The majority of them are sent to hospitals or institutions where they are processed out of existence with cool precision and emotional detachment so characteristic of space-age life. Many terminally ill patients and elderly persons are losing the privilege (right) of dying at home. They are no longer the center of attention in their final days. Removed from their families, they are losing their social roles. Human beings have always feared death and modern man prefers to deny death's existence as much as possible. Death is almost un-American, contrary to our worship of youth, optimism and the healthy pursuit of happiness. We ignore how terrified many patients are of the loneliness, dreaded more than death, that precedes the final moments.

"People should die at home," said one of our staff doctors. "Families worry about the medical problems, but in most cases they are not difficult. In five minutes anyone can learn to give a shot. Medication can take care of the pain. The family's biggest problem is maintaining the physical stamina it takes to care for someone who is ill."

There is not much you can do wrong medically and a lot you can do right psychologically by caring for patients at home. Dying persons need to be close to people, have their hand held and simply be touched.

"The purpose of my work is not to help a patient die. It is to help him live until he dies. . . . In America, terminal patients are treated like 'the thing,' " says Dr. Elizabeth Kübler-Ross (*On Death and Dying*, Macmillan Company).

Well-known through taped interviews, television programs, and her fascinating book are the *five stages of dying* worked out by Doctor Ross. They are not exact steps so much as clusters of experience made clear to us through interviews with dying patients. Sudden or violent or accidental deaths apart, most patients will come to terms with death along lines like these five steps—give or take an overlap or skipping.

Patients often react to news of serious illness with a "no, not me" attitude. You are into the drama of denial, and it takes many forms. Once this defense is dropped, anger often follows with a "Why me?" protest. At our hospital we often notice this among young people who feel that life is ending before it has even started. Look for a rather critical, nasty, troublesome behavior pattern to develop. The third stage will likely be a bargaining phase of "Yes, me, all right, but. . . ." Deals with God or people around them will likely be forthcoming. Promise almost anything but get a reprieve from the onslaught of pain and death is the script being written. There follows so often a fourth stage which is "Yes, me, and maybe soon." This brings on depression and silent crying into pillows. We would all do well to "feel with" such tears.

Patients have told me what drives them to a frenzy about this stage is some staff member or relative bustling in cheerfully to announce: "Things aren't so bad now, are they? We'll have you up and around in no time." The mental verbalizing of patients at such moments is not printable.

If more of us or even some of us give true support and help prepare our patient through compassionate listening, he or she may reach the final stage of acceptance. This amounts to: "Yes, me, for my time is near and I'm ready." This is more than just being resigned to cruel fate. It is very much like Jesus on the Cross yielding up his soul with, "It is finished." For in this last stage patients sever the ties of earth and are ready to welcome the end—and join the Risen Christ.

If we have done our homework as ministering agents of God's love, we will share with the patient this peace-bringing acceptance. They will often amaze us with things which they can teach us about God, about life's goals and rewards, and about phony dreams which we are pursuing. One friend of mine kindly but firmly shook up a priest trying to give comfort with good-cheer platitudes by saying: "Father, talk to me about God."

An elderly patient who was ready to meet God queried me: "Do I need all these big deals I'm getting? Is it wrong for me to want to die and meet God?" So I let him talk it out, then told him of Paul wishing to be dissolved and be with Christ and the ancient prophet telling God, "Enough is enough; now take my life." So he smiled and said: "No more of those super-duper treatments to drag out a few more hours." Now who is going to say his death-wish was out of order?

Certainly many excellent theologians would back him up by telling us of three kinds of therapy: Natural, ordinary, extraordinary. The natural ones would be preserving life by normal nursing care—feeding medication orally to relieve pain, insomnia, even mental anguish. Ordinary means would be an extension of these natural ones to include common clinical procedures—the common techniques of modern surgery and medicine. Nobody gets too disturbed about these types.

Then come the extraordinary means, the kind not readily or usually available. They are not likely to cure and they may be only experimental in nature.

While it remains unlikely that they will reverse the dying process, the patient or his family will find them to be really expensive, often very painful and sometimes downright repugnant. It is agreed among modern moralists that for a dying patient only ordinary means of treatment need to be employed. So out go the super-dupers.

When should such treatments be stopped, if once started? Who decides? Is murder or suicide involved in terminating extraordinary methods with no (or quite doubtful) curative value and which only prolong the process of dying? No, there is neither murder nor suicide. And we should all remember this so that doctors, families and even patients are not blamed unfairly. Both suicide and murder are direct positive acts of destruction or omission of *ordinary* means to maintain life.

Life magazine ran a story in its January 14, 1972, issue about "The Right To Die." One of the examples told of Tony Gallo and the kidney machine that kept him alive—at a cost he decided was not worth paying. He ripped the tubes from his arm and walked out of the treatment room. His wife pleaded with him to go back on the machine, telling him it was a sin to give up (It was not a sin objectively for Tony to refuse this extraordinary means). He stuck to his decision and a week later he was dead.

The saddest part of the story to me was the wife so torn by her doubts that she said: "Tony should have fought harder. We don't have the right to do that. We have to let God take us in his time. . . . But I don't think Tony will be judged wrong for what he did. It's against the church, yes, but look at the suffering he went through."

Perhaps by now some understanding spiritual counselor has told Tony's wife: "It is not and never was against the church. For God expects what is possible for our strength and judges us in the context of the usual and ordinary." A Chancery Office official in Florida wrote the editor a few weeks later of the church's teaching as we have explained it here. How many subscribers of *Life* saw this correct interpretation?

It is quite understandable that doctors and nurses, trained to see death as the enemy they must defeat at all costs, regularly resort to heroic measures to keep patients alive. Often this means radical surgery or the employment of complex machines that keep a flicker of life in people so old or ravaged as to be beyond caring. We need closer bonds between theology and medicine to emphasize moral principles that help patients. Priests, families and patients should articulate clearly and emphatically to medical people their wishes and decisions about extraordinary methods of therapy and service.

Perhaps we need a new discipline in medicine, what Dr. William Poe of Duke University calls "marantology" (from a Greek word meaning *withered* or *wasted*). Marantologists would care for those whom no one else wants, those who have "committed the sin of remaining alive but not yielding to our manipulations. . . . A marantology service could be a place a person could die in dignity without all the bother death engenders elsewhere" (*New England Journal of Medicine* as in *Time*, March 13, 1972).

The doctor makes clear in his article that patients object to being cycled and recycled from doctor to hospital to specialist—with no reasonable future. He emphasizes that he is against euthanasia, but also that there is a limit to what we ought to do to prolong life. Perhaps if more doctors thought like that it would help people see death as a friend—and help them extend their vision beyond life into eternity.

Despite our honest determination to minister to sick people, there comes a fearful moment of decision about *telling* the patient. Do we let the physician impart a diagnosis couched in terms like "severe" or "advancing" or "progressive" illness? Do we let close relatives tell the patient "the truth?" Should the attending clergyman come through with "the truth?" Maybe Dr. Bernard Meyer of New York was right when he answered: "Which patient and what truth?"

All words have different meanings for different people. Think of the many kinds of cancer known to science. Tell a physician he is afflicted with "basal cell carcinoma" on his cheek and he relaxes with the truth.

He knows it's the most benign of cancers. Tell an unlettered housewife the same truth in the same words about herself, and you might get suicidal reactions. "To tell the truth" means first assessing carefully the patient's and the family's understanding of disease and of certain medical terms and also their intellectual and emotional patterns. Then, scientifically, artistically and wisely a picture of what is involved can be presented—ignoring or even denying talk of an early fatal outcome. Medical people, and certainly the rest of us, really do not *know* what will happen to *this* patient. But they can convey by word, gesture and actions that they consider him as being alive; and they will strive to keep him alive with all the devotion, science and ardor that they would bring to patients with less severe illnesses.

Doctors and nurses tell us that so often the patients arrive at their own awareness of the seriousness of their illness, before being told. They appreciate that families call in a clergyman early. Old stories die hard, but absolution and the sacrament of the sick (as we now call the anointing) are accepted more easily these days as curative and comforting. Mistaking the priest for the undertaker will not happen if we have listened and shared with sick people their transition through the five stages of death mentioned earlier. Most Catholics have said the *Hail Mary* countless times a year. "Pray for us now and at the hour of our death" are words they feel will bring Mary's powerful help to them. We who minister to the sick should not hesitate to pray them with the sick.

Most of us say that we would want to be told the whole truth if we had an illness that was critical. Why then do so many medical people refuse to tell a patient he has terminal cancer? Because we must always maintain hope? Sure, but does hope mean only trust in a miraculous cure? Yet as one dying patient recently said: "That's not the only kind of hope. We hope for good care, for relief from pain, that our families will be provided for. And we need hope for a peaceful and holy death."

There is no justification for lying to patients and medical statements filled with technical language that is misleading double talk ends up as a big lie. A conspiracy of silence and deceit is an inhuman way to live or die. We see too much degrading and dehumanizing "managing" of lives these days. The dying patients we wish to help do not need managing. They need to be cared for lovingly.

Could you look cancer in the eye and face it down? The famous Father Daniel Lord, S.J., did just that a few years ago. A few months after doctors told him he had cancer of both lungs, he wrote an article that was picked up by magazines across America and Canada. In it he said: "When the verdict was cancer, I was relieved. I had expected to die some day of heart trouble or a stroke, and I dreaded the sudden and perhaps sacramentless death. Cancer seemed kindly. I liked the gentle warning" (Thomas Gavin, S.J., Union City, New Jersey, in *The Sign*, July 1969).

Then, this whirlwind of activity, remembered with love by so many Catholics across America, plunged into new books, articles, lectures, two mammoth pageants for Detroit and Toronto and several retreats. He brought fresh hope and courage to thousands of people suffering from cancer. Determined to use well the time left to him, he found his whole outlook on life sharpened, every moment more precious, each day a thing to be hoarded. This man had made sanctity a joyous thing to three generations of Catholic youth. And yet the greatest lesson he ever taught was *acceptance* before death.

So the lessons in dying go on around us daily. We must learn to listen, to share in compassion, to learn from courage shown by others. We human beings are one family, each needing to be redeemed, and yet each helping to redeem, as Mary did, in sharing Calvary with Christ.

CHAPTER SIX

Beyond the Dying

> Joseph of Arimathaea . . . boldly went to Pilate and asked
> for the body of Jesus. . . . He granted the corpse to Joseph
> who bought a shroud, took Jesus down from the cross. . . .
> Mark 15: 43-46

One of the last great sculptures done by
Michelangelo was *The Deposition*. It shows Nicode-
mus helping to remove Christ from the cross. He gave
features reminiscent of his own to the cowled face
that is relaxed with compassion for the dead Christ.

The greatest sculpture of his youth was the *Pietá*
(until recently, preserved intact as one of the world's
finest masterpieces in St. Peter's basilica in Rome).
The sorrow of Mary is conveyed with a single gesture—an outstretched left hand. Christ, though dead,
seems very lifelike. Indeed, the risen Christ will con-

quer death. Mary looks bigger than life and even younger than Christ. Her towering sanctity and purity thus emerge.

Artists so often are great theologians. Thoughts inspired by the gospel story of events following the crucifixion and reflections on works like Michelangelo's Pietá support us through the sadness following death. For we must let ourselves and others grieve, allowing everyone to work through and talk through their loss. Only after such cleansing of the emotions does the healing of time take effect.

Again we suggest that people learn from Mary's acceptance of losing Christ. How could any mother not deeply mourn the brutal death inflicted on her son by people for whom he did only good? Yet Mary would neither blame nor be hostile nor seek retribution. Behind the agonies inflicted upon Christ's body lay the loving design of salvation for humanity which the Father wrought through Christ's surrender.

However death comes, we must train ourselves to see it as the fulfillment of life. Sadly enough, we are surrounded with customs and attitudes which cover death with a thick blanket of uncertainty and unreality. Instead of the naturalness of burial in a wooden coffin and going back to dust in our graves, we are likely to be embalmed, powdered and preserved in the phoniest of fashions in expensively lined caskets of indestructible metal. Often the mourners are not even allowed to see the hole dug for burial.

The results of this kind of denial of death is that people do not come to terms with truth. The person mourned is gone and new patterns of life must develop. That is why mourning is important. It is good evidence that finalities are being accepted. In homes and at wakes we all do the grieving relatives and friends a favor by letting them pour out their grief. Their healthy release leads to new strength. Many of our physicians should cease giving so much medication to dull feelings.

Living with illness and its results should make us aware that there is something divine shared in every man. Often we can help unlock hidden resources in dying persons by helping them deal with terminal illness. Many times too we can help grieving persons take on nobility in grief by letting them pour out what they feel. To listen, to share, but especially to be sincere—even without a word—should be a golden rule for viewings in public or wakes at home.

So seldom do most of us keep in mind that persons in grief are struggling with emotional turmoil, shock, numbness of mind and possibly guilt. We are visiting people dealing with a type of illness—the mourning process. How cruel then to project our petty concerns or our phony dramatics to get attention. Most of us have seen or dealt with quasi-professional weepers who enjoy wakes to the hilt. If we have ever been irritated, amused or bored with their antics, then let us pay heed to our own behavior. The touchy arguments, the fighting for place and esteem of onlookers, the catty remarks, the cliques gathering to gossip—all are as unworthy at a wake as they would have been on Calvary.

To comfort the sorrowful is a beautiful work of mercy. Coming from the love of God and neighbor it needs no glorification of self. Let our words and actions reflect empathy, feeling what the bereaved feel. If we felt little or nothing we could at least be honest in saying: "I can't know your suffering, but am sorry, I'll pray for you."

Many persons have told priests of the many wishy-washy nothings muttered to them at wakes. Perhaps the emptiest of these is the one voiced far too often: "If there's anything I can do, let me know." It sounds good; it is harmless; and it may even seem helpful. But it's an empty nothing. If we can volunteer something specific—use my car; I'll send over a baby-sitter; let me take your place—very good. Otherwise, we should keep quiet until we can. Who needs promises and more promises?

When another suffers, we cannot remove his cross and put it on our own shoulders. The function of compassion is rather to give to another person supportive love. Help him bring out his own power to bear grief with dignity. It is almost like feeling "I'll cry with her and I'll also be there to help wipe away her tears." We need not to be afraid to give comfort by tenderly offering our hand or putting a loving arm about a sagging shoulder. The language of such contact means "I really care."

We need not to be afraid to try to identify with those who suffer. To put yourself in their place helps you feel things they like to share. "I remember how dark and uncertain things were for me when I lost my father," when said naturally, will help your friend discuss his loss. And often he needs just such talk. One mother who lost her youngster in a fire said one of the hardest things to bear was the hush-hush attitude around her. "I needed and wanted to talk about her. But if I tried, somebody would change the subject. This really hurt."

In the minds and hearts of those grieving must be awareness of how close are Jesus and Mary. They both knew the feelings of desolation that human hearts endure. The loud cries and tears of Jesus on the

cross were wrung from a heart conscious of an aloneness that included bewilderment at the inscrutable
ways of God. Puzzled that seemingly even his Father
had deserted him, Jesus felt utterly abandoned. No
other human knew this as well as Mary in the three
days' loss. Simple as it sounds, the best prayer in
bereavement is: "Help me, Jesus and Mary, just to
hold on, to believe and to trust in God at the blackest
of moments."

Here in America we need badly to revise our customs for mourning and burying our dead. A few
years back all of us, especially morticians, were quite
shaken up by Evelyn Waugh's social satire on burial
customs in *The Loved One*. Then they received another jolt from Jessica Mitford in *The American Way
of Death* and its masterfully accurate exposé of "the
high cost of dying." In the soaring sixties with Vatican II's reforms and renewals, it seemed that we were
entering a promising period and moving toward a
new day, a resurrection of truly Christian burial
practices.

Reform of "the system" has not come yet. But it begins by each individual trying to act like a believer in death as an entrance into resurrection glory with Christ. We need awareness of the joy and peace that follow sorrow which is borne bravely in imitation of Christ and Mary.

CHAPTER SEVEN

Life Must Go on

> So Joseph took the body, wrapped it in a clean shroud, and put it in his own new tomb which he had hewn out of the rock. He then rolled a large stone across the entrance of the tomb.
>
> Matt. 27: 59-61

The tomb was sealed. Christ was buried. Mary was alone, deprived of the physical presence of Jesus, deprived even of his dead body. Mary surely must have experienced then what occurs to each of us when our loved one returns to the earth from which he came. The feeling remains: "Why must life go on? If only I could be with him in risen glory?"

As one bereaved wife explained to me: "Through his long months of terminal illness, we shared everything in heart and mind. I became like a person dying, almost one foot in the grave. Now I am wrenched back to the earthy things of this world. And a thousand things demand attention, things that had slipped into unimportance before.

There are many ways of saying it but each individual has his own way of feeling it and coming to terms with it. It is the process of taking up life again while still in mourning, a painful period indeed, but absolutely necessary for the mental and physical health of the bereaved. Mourning cannot be short-circuited nor should it be—despite well-intentioned advice about getting involved, stop thinking back, get busy and enjoy yourself. Perhaps feverish funeral preparations and wake-funeral activities only serve to delay the total impact of death—we are like one in shock.

The inevitable moment comes when the mourner faces being alone. And he must feel it, live through it. For someone who has been a part of his life will never tangibly be so again. Even Mary went through this, aware though she was of Christ's victory over death. Mary was a childless widow and knew to a preeminent degree the pains of aloneness those words express. She knew our desolation in the mourning we must live through. Let us strive to learn about her wellsprings of strength that we may tap them for our growth.

The days running into months following the crucifixion must have seen Mary in meditation upon his words from the cross. He had taught a complete philosophy for suffering and she had listened and learned. There had actually been a wedding on Calvary. Mary had stood beneath the cross as the symbol and personification of the church—the Bride of Christ. Mary was the Mother of Christ, but in this new divine life which we call grace Mary was his bride, the New Eve, partner to the New Adam, joining her bridegroom in the redemption of mankind.

That wedding feast that began with his sacrificial death continues through the Sacrifice of the Mass. Christ had taught his followers at the Last Supper that they must do always in his memory what he had done.

Here, then, above all else, is the source of strength for all who mourn, for all who dread taking up life again, who are fearful that they must soon again suffer through agonies of dying and death. Mary knew that Jesus would never be with her again on this earth in the way that he had been. But he would be with her—and with every member of the church—through each Sacrifice-Banquet-Memorial which we call the Mass. We too in the Mass share the new wine of the Holy Spirit flowing from the open side of Christ and eat his flesh to support the weakness of our own bodies through our sacrifices.

Our devotion to Mary—however we pour it out in prayer—must go right to the heart of Christian faith. Our sharing in Mass must make us one with Christ. Both Christ and Mary will teach us in the depths of our person what it means that "life must go on." Christ spoke of his life as "doing what my Father wills." Mary spoke of her life as "may God do with me what he wills." They both teach us that life is good if it is given as a gift of love. They both want us to give our lives in love to show forth love for all men.

They want us to understand as best we can the suffering we see experienced by persons all around us. They want us to show unfailing solicitude for people who need kindness and help. We must do as Mary did at the wedding feast at Cana in Galilee— help an embarrassed couple solve a very human problem, a problem small enough for most people to miss but large enough for Jesus to accomplish his first public miracle. And we can be sure that they want us to begin acting in these patterns, as soon as we have reasonably worked our way through our mourning.

The normal and natural processes of feeling hopeless, empty, even despairing must be experienced and not denied. It helps to tell ourselves that the pain will stop and we will have a newly productive life once again. Even the confusing anger felt toward the departed—why did he leave me alone now, with all these problems?—will pass. It is best to admit the reality of this anger, accept it as average and then dismiss it.

A special cross to bear during the months (or more) of mourning is the insensitive, clumsy or even crass attempts by others to "console" us. Widowers have told me of phone calls within days after the funeral from lonely women seeking dates. And widows talk often of enduring pain from the attitudes and "offers" of male friends, not to speak of the widow's problem of being treated as a fifth wheel in social gatherings, even as a husband-stealer by women who have been friends for years. Such things can happen but they only show our inexperience in handling grief.

Perhaps your return from witnessing a cemetery burial will be a return to nursing a handicapped child, a senile parent or another patient in your home. Perhaps you now find yourself alone with your own fragile health as your daily cross: The disabling injury that has you limping or walking in pain, the chronic ailment that plagues your days and causes

sleepless nights, the operation you need but post-
poned through the days devoted to your dying spouse
—these are all very real situations.

"Sometimes I feel I'm just not going to ever really
be well again," said one patient to me. This gentle
complaint came after several doctors had talked of
countless possible helps. But the debilitating illness
continued and this patient felt like the chronic cases
who are told "you'll just have to live with it." Many
who suffer long illnesses begin to feel like the para-
lytic patients creeping inch by inch back to partial
mobility, the blind struggling with Braille and seeing-
eye dogs, or the paraplegics battling self-pity and
unconscious cruelty to achieve progress.

This whole book is meant to induce reflections that
help each of us to live with or minister to illness in its
myriad forms. Inner motivations are so personal and
who can tell another how to live courageously, bear
manfully, hang in there? Yes those who suffer teach
us that pain is meaningless without God. Yet pain
is always a healing force when endured for Christ

and offered to God in union with Christ. Yesterday's pain is gone; tomorrow's is not here. Use today's pain, the sacrament of this moment, to help redeem yourself and other human beings. Like Mary, you are a coredeemer.